"Part Mark Twain, part Bill Cosby, part C.S Lewis, D. Roderick Thomas is a breath of fresh air in a stressful and often lifeless world. Come join the thousands who have fallen in love with this sightless storyteller and his charming little Trinidad village."

"These are some sweet, small-town tales that are as comfy and relaxing as a cool Caribbean breeze on a hot summer day."

"I've rarely heard hometown tales presented with such fun and humor. Thomas helps us to put our everyday struggles and hardships into perspective— all the while laughing ourselves to life."

It's all true, if I do have to say so myself.

D. Roderick Thomas

Messy Revival

Funny Stories for a Change

D. Roderick Thomas

Printed in the USA
Print management by AB Publishing.

All Scripture references are from the New American
Standard Version.

Cover design and artwork by Jonathan Henderson and
Preston Davis.

Text design by Greg Solie • AltamontGraphics.com

ISBN: 978-1-61539-142-4

*I*n the interest of maintaining confidentiality and respect
for the individuals who are described in this book, I've
changed some names, transported some people—and
even some really good stories—and relocated them to my little
village. I can't always remember exactly what folks said, though
the lessons are clear as day, and the funny things they did can
still make me laugh.

—D. Roderick Thomas

Contents

Acknowledgements
Big Thanks

I first want to thank Jenny Thomas. You did a heck of a good job raising D. Roderick Thomas. To my favorite brother, David, and my crazy sisters, Gilly, Marie Ann, and Dianne: In hindsight, perhaps I ought to thank you for allowing me to tell your business without your permission. When people ask, I'll say I made it all up. Jonathan Henderson, your confidence both in me and my creative genius goes a long way. I didn't put my mug all over the front cover like you would have wanted me to, but if you help me with the next book maybe I will. Iris Henderson, your editorial prowess has taken this manuscript a long way. To my Stockton sister Dr. Khandie Waugh: You're a breath of fresh Jamaican air. Girl, you hooked me up. To my best friend and sister Suzanne Thomas Douglas, and my niece and nephew Ekechi and Nkechi: I don't know why I'm writing your names in this section, but thanks. You claimed to have read my book, so that should count for something. Kaisha, even though you only read two pages, you still get a shout out. To Clifford Cromwell, the sage who sees eye to eye with me: All those hours you've spent pouring wisdom into my life will never be in vain. Thanks to Leon and Julie Brown: It was the risk you took in providing me the opportunity to do my first Bay Area comedy show at your church that was the genesis of this book. To my members and friends MJ,

7

Jordan Montgomery, Jessica Jacobie, and Susan Yearbro: You moved me from corny to cute. The professional editorial assistance I have received is amazing: Elyse Weingarten, Jessica McFerson, Renee Johnson, Collin Garraway, Petranella LaFluer, and Margaret Dana. Big thanks to my main editor who brought this whole thing together and took me home, Pastor France Marcott. France, you have always been one of those larger-than-life persons in my experience. You truly are the embodiment of the art of thriving.

Introduction

Welcome to Locoville

I spent most of my early years in a bright orange and green house on the corner of Cuckoo Drive in Locoville, Trinidad, West Indies. The unique choice of color elevated the house's standing in the village. When giving directions, people would say, "Two blocks from the bright orange house, make a left." All the problematic things you may have heard about living in corner houses are true. You know everyone's business and, in turn, attract village gossip and other foolishness like a magnet. So, on any given day, sitting around our dinner table or hanging out in our back yard, you could find gamblers, winos, gluttons, and pranksters.

Even though I was born blind, I was only able to convince my family of this around the age of seven. This is when I started breaking dishes so that my load of chores would be lightened. The experts now say that I'm legally blind. That means I can't have a driver's license, but it hasn't stopped me from driving! Locoville people considered me only "conveniently" blind, and weren't inclined to cut me any slack.

These are some funny stories from growing up in my little village among crooks and clowns. There were guys like Silkie Stern, who could sell Caribbean sea breeze in a bag, and my best childhood friend Jarvis, who didn't know how to stay out of trouble. My sister Gilly kept us entertained with all the creative tricks she tried for getting the winning lottery numbers, and Ma Pearl dazzled Locoville with her so-called mystical powers. The terrible twins shook things up with all their mischief, and Mavis and Big Frank were a pain in the neck with their constant bickering. As for me, since I get to tell the story, I was, with out a doubt, the most honest, well-behaved kid in the village. (Anything you hear to the contrary is just a tall tale.) These characters all came together one summer under the preaching tent. It's no surprise that what happened next was a messy revival.

Chapter 1
Funny Scary Stories

I grew up in a very superstitious culture. I recall spending long fearful nights being entertained by folktale horror stories.[1] Author Stephen King had nothing on Aunt Eerie and her scary ghost stories. These stories were so frightening and real that many nights my brother David and I slept over at our grumpy old aunt's house in order to avoid walking home alone in the dark. Whenever we were forced to walk home we would sing hymns as loudly as we could, finally arriving worn out with sore throats. Looking back at those spooky nights, I think Aunt Eerie told those stories to keep us at her house so that her household chores would get done. That crooked old woman!

Those horror stories helped to explain the reasons for all our superstitious practices. There was a *soucouyant*, which is a person who turned into a ball of fire and came to suck your blood during the night—sort of like a vampire. When villagers woke up with blue marks on their skin, they always blamed the *soucouyant*. This belief in the *soucouyant* served me well at times, since I could wrestle with the boys at school and blame the *soucouyant* for the scratches. To ward off the *soucouyant*, people had to put salt under a chair. Or if you wanted to catch one and suspected a neighbor or family member, you turned a broom upside down before they came in your home, supposedly making it difficult for them to get up and leave. Creepy, huh?

Then there was the *jumbie*, a dark-looking spirit that followed you home and scared the living daylights out of you. If you came in after midnight, you had to enter your house backwards and make the sign of the cross on your forehead and chest to keep it out of your home. Otherwise, it could kidnap you from your family and you'd be gone forever. My three oldest sisters, Dianne, Marie-Anne, and Gilly, who often snuck out and back in through the bathroom window to go to late night parties, had obviously perfected the art of warding off *jumbies*.

All these superstitions, in one way or another, were built on dealing with the dead and making pacts with the devil, so it was no surprise that cemeteries were places of our greatest fear. They were so scary that, as children, we were warned, even when just driving by, to never point a finger at it, or else the finger would rot and fall off.

Late one afternoon, Silkie Stern was hiding in the cemetery eating the mangoes he had stolen from his neighbor's tree. As Silkie was sucking on his third mango, celebrating his masterful thievery, he heard voices coming from behind the tombstone facing him.

"You have this one."

"No, I'll have *this* one."

"No, no, no, you take *that* one; *I* want this one."

"This one looks real juicy; I'm going to eat him."

Silkie dropped everything, and faster than the Jamaican sprinter Eusane Bolt, he was out of that place. The terrible twins, Tim and Tommy were startled by Silkie's sudden dash, since they, too, were dividing the spoil of their own stolen mangoes. They looked up in panic to see someone running away from the tombstone as fast as he could go.

"Do you think he saw us?" Tommy asked.

"Nah. That's only Silkie Stern. No big deal. Now, you have that one." Timmy said.

"Yeah that's fat and round. I'll take it."

It was around this time that Pastor Charles Livermore came from New York City to carry out a four-week church revival in Locoville for the congregation of the Better Living Believers. They put up a green and white tent on the soccer field and held nightly services. In his first message, the pastor read from the Bible that a wise man named Solomon claimed that the dead don't know anything. They can no longer love, hate, or be envious. And worst yet, they have no memory and don't even know that they are dead.[2] Though the pastor was quite persuasive, no one could convince Silkie that it hadn't been two dead people fighting over him at the cemetery.

Chapter 2
With All That Mystical Power

Aunt Eerie would tell us that people have been afraid of the dead for a long time. She told the story of an old woman named Mother Eve who, a long time ago, got tricked bad. She lived in a garden and her father told her not to eat from the tree in the middle of that garden or else she would die. But one day she started talking to this really pretty snake and, boy, did it mess with her mind! Auntie said that this snake was called a serpent and that it had the power to trick people who didn't listen to their parents. So the serpent told Mother Eve that if she ate the fruit she wouldn't really die.[3] "You'll sorta die," the serpent said, "but you'll not be fully dead." This is why everybody in Locoville believed that dead people were not really dead.

An old lady in the village whom we called Ma Pearl made a great deal of money off of this belief. Ma Pearl was known as an *obeah* woman, the island version of a witch doctor or psychic. On other islands, *obeah* is called voodoo. She claimed to have the power to cast spells on people, separate married couples, and help you get whichever spouse you desired. My sister Gilly said that she never trusted any of them because no *obeah* person ever gave her the winning lottery numbers.

Most obeah people lived in tiny shacks on the backside of nowhere, and you had to cross a river, climb up a hill on a winding trail, and push through a lot of brush before you were able to get to them. However, one summer, a group of us sold books to raise money for a school trip to Barbados. I unsuspectingly entered a store to sell my books, and later found out it was owned and managed by Ma Pearl. Her specialty was selling magical potions. The labels on the products amazed me like, "How to Keep Your Man" powder and "She'll Come Back to You" lotion. In addition to these, she offered many services, from telling your future to reading your palms or communicating with dead relatives. Her business had really begun booming once she started repackaging her products with these clever labels.

When my dad died, my uncle Ruse got a great big carton of sugar water from Ma Pearl to sprinkle on the walls so we'd be able to send Daddy messages. The sugar water was so expensive that Uncle Ruse had to swap our pet goat Shane for the potion.

Many of Ma Pearl's clients began attending the Better Living Revival under the tent. The pastor said that God didn't want people to go to *obeah* men or women for answers to their problems in life because God Himself would provide.[4] The pastor stamped his feet and pounded the podium as he said, "If anyone claims to be talking to your dead relatives, they're not your dead relatives but demons!"

After the first week of the revival, Ma Pearl began to hear about this man of God's preaching when many of her customers stopped doing business with her. Ma Pearl flew into a vicious rage and wrote the pastor a letter telling him that if he didn't pack up and leave town immediately he would be disfigured or dead by the end of the week. The pastor took it upon himself to battle it out with Ma Pearl. He read the letter to the jam-packed tent that night and challenged Ma Pearl to see whose power was stronger. The key word here would be D-R-A-M-A. From then on Locoville was filled with it. Some folks began crying and praying aloud for this ignorant preacher who didn't know of Ma Pearl's powers. Others quietly slipped out from the tent lest some of Ma Pearl's curses would miss the pastor and spill over onto them. Despite all this, he continued to preach.

The next morning, the pastor woke up to a coffin with a black rose on it sitting at the doorway of his cottage. Those who woke up early to go to the market, seeing this sign of death, crossed to the other side of the street in fear of what the pastor might suffer. Now, this man should be given some credit. He really believed in God's power and had a healthy sense of humor. That day, he went down to the funeral home and bought a larger coffin and a dozen black roses and had them placed at the entrance of Ma Pearl's business.

Two weeks later, when I just happened to be in the vicinity of Ma Pearl's store, I found it closed with a chain over the door! In Trinidad, that meant eviction. I guess Ma Pearl, with all her *obeah* and professed mystical powers, couldn't foresee that eviction notice.[5]

Chapter 3
Billy in Three Places

I had always been confused about what happened to people after they died. When I was about nine years old, Billy, who lived in the gray and white house by the river, died from pneumonia. He had been about eleven years old and could play a mean game of cricket. Cricket, invented by the British, is the original way of playing baseball. Billy was what we call in the cricketing world an "all rounder," which is someone who is good at both batting and pitching. Unlike the other thugs who caused a brawl whenever their team lost, Billy was a peacemaker.

At Billy's funeral service, Pastor Swindle, the minister from Milk and Honey Tabernacle, preached a sermon that was quite confusing. At one point, he said, "As you can see, Billy looks quite peaceful lying in the coffin." At another part, he told us, "Billy is now in heaven looking down on us." Then somewhere near the end of his sermon, he lifted his voice and said, "When Jesus comes, He'll call Billy from the grave." I was totally at a loss! How could Billy be in three places at the same time? Was he lying in the coffin, in heaven, or waiting for Jesus to call him from the grave? My brother David, suddenly an expert, explained that when good people died, they became like the trinity and could be in three places at the same time.

Two years later, my dad died. At the last count, my dad had fifteen children, with me supposedly being the last of the bunch. My aunts told me that I was an old man's child. At his funeral, I met a couple of strange women who, crying uncontrollably, kept saying, "Daddy, why did you leave us?" *Did they just call him Daddy?* Not the best place to meet new siblings, right?

My half-brother Mike wanted to take my mind off my grief, so he took his blind little brother on a water-bike ride. I paddled the water bike in the deep blue water of Store Bay Tobago, closely following my brother's voice. With every major wave, I was washed off the water bike. Thank God for life jackets. Years later, Mike shared with me that he was scared to death and kept asking himself, "Man, what was I thinking, bringing a blind boy on his own water bike?" As my legs grew numb and the waves kept knocking me off, I asked Mike, "How far are we from the shore?"

He replied, "It's only a few minutes away."

Then, when I heard a boat racing past us, I asked myself, *Do boats speed like this in the shallows?* In a quiet moment when I finally had some balance and the waves were still, Mike said to me, "Dex, Daddy is looking down on us."

What good does that do me? Thinking of the long distance to the shore, and the bumpy ride ahead, I wondered, *Man, couldn't Dad calm the waves and get us to shore more quickly? Wouldn't that be more helpful? What use is it to just sit in heaven looking down on us?*

Sometimes I used this idea of Dad looking down on us from heaven to my advantage. Since my brother David was always bigger and stronger than me, I could never wrestle with him and win. So I resorted to using my mind to whoop him instead. Whenever he thumped me, I'd say with tears in my eyes, "Daddy is looking down at you from heaven, and you're making him sad while he's in a happy place." This line worked every time!

Billy in Three Places?

Across the street from the barber was a red and blue parrot in the window of Silkie Stern's pet shop. Silkie assured me that this was the last of its kind in the world and that it spoke three different languages. However, the parrot was on a break and so he couldn't demonstrate its talent right then and there. Only $28.75 and it could be all mine! The other parrots were $5.50, but who wanted those when I could be the owner of a truly unique bird? But where would an eleven-year-old find all that money? I wondered why in the world I did not save my money? *Well,* I thought, *there is no use getting worked up over yesterday's losses.* I needed to find a way to get that bird!

Unlike me, David, saved like it was nobody's business. He would sometimes walk home from school in order to save his taxi fare. If he only knew how badly Daddy wanted me to get that parrot! With tears in my eyes, I told him that Dad saw the parrot and thought it would look better in my room than in the pet shop. And each day that the parrot remained in the pet shop it made Daddy's heart so unhappy. I loved how that boy loved his living dead father! David was not in the best of moods when he wiped out his entire savings, counting out $28.75 for the purchase of my prized pet. I had struck gold!

That afternoon I cleared a special place and re-arranged my room for my new, long-desired, very special occupant. Because the shop closed at 5 pm, we decided to get the bird first thing in the morning. That night at the preaching revival, the New York preacher Pastor Livermore gave the sermon that got him into trouble with Ma Pearl, explaining that dead people were not in heaven or hell. He said, "No one goes to a better place as soon as they die." He told a story about a time when Jesus stood outside of a tomb where His good friend Lazarus lie dead. Jesus shouted, "Lazarus, come out!" and the dead man came back to life. "You would think that since Lazarus was such a good friend of Jesus, he should have been in heaven. Then Jesus would have simply said, 'Lazarus, come down.' But Lazarus was in the grave, out cold in a deep sleep," declared Pastor Livermore. He shared several other Bible verses showing that dead people were not in heaven, hell, or limbo, but rather in the grave like Lazarus was. [6]

For the first time in his life, David was all ears in church and lights were turning on in his head. The pastor said that this dude in the Bible named Job, who was the most righteous person in his village, said that when he died, the grave would be his home. I have never seen an evil eye before, but the stare I felt from David made my bones shiver. If looks could kill, I would have been dead. As David kicked me on the shin, I remembered that he had to lead me home after the revival meeting. There are consequences to being both blind and crooked! I started praying that the pastor would end his sermon with people's need to forgive others or this wouldn't be a very funny story.

Chapter 4
The Good Book

I grew up knowing the Bible was a special and sacred book. We were taught that it was wrong to put another book on top of it. People placed it at the center of their coffee tables and would wash their hands before opening it. It was almost as if they worshipped the book itself. But some of the Better Living Believers had figured out that they didn't actually need to *know* the Bible to come off sounding like a smart Christian. They'd confidently toss around an adage like, "As the Bible says, 'Cleanliness is next to godliness.'" Or, "Just like it says in the Bible, 'If it ain't broke don't fix it.'"

Unfortunately for me, the school for the blind didn't have the complete Braille Bible, so I only got the Bible in bits. Eventually, when I did get all the pieces, my Bible was the size of 18 big, thick, encyclopedia books! I couldn't tuck my Bible under my arm while walking to church like most people. If someone reminded me, "Don't forget your Bible," I would have needed a pickup truck.

When I finally got all 18 volumes, I didn't care about how it looked on my coffee table. I really wanted to understand what was *in* the book. Pastor Livermore would say, "The Bible is God's recipe for happiness in life. And He knows a thing or two about happiness since He happens to be the one who created it.[7] It's like God gave a handbook to humans so they would understand how to get the most out of life."

Jarvis understood the pastor's analogy to mean that if God hadn't given us the Bible for direction, we would have to fend for ourselves. "It would be like buying your Aunt Eerie the latest computer without showing her how to use it. It's just as bad as when your dad didn't have the instruction manual and tried to use the DVD tray as a cup holder."

I became so hungry to know about God, I was even eating up those dull and repetitive family trees in the books of Numbers and Chronicles. One night my mom stuck her head into my room and saw me reading my Braille Bible in the dark. Switching the lights on she said, "Boy, why are you so silly, reading there in the dark?"

I replied, "Only because I can read with my eyes closed!" Then her own light came on and she left.

During the second night of the revival, Pastor Livermore explained that, when we read the Bible, we exchange opinions with God about how best to live life. He taught, "Try God's idea on loving your enemies; it's the biggest stress reliever out there."[8] And, "Have a go at not lying and you'll see that people will actually start trusting you."[9]

He explained that those big, complicated words that preachers use, like "transformation," "conversion" and "newness of life" were simply ways of talking about how to accept and live out God's ideas. However, what really motivated me to read the Bible was something I learned when Tania, a very fine girl, transferred as a new student to Locoville High School during my senior year.

She was the envy of all the other girls in the village and the desire of all the guys. She was a bit nerdy, but who pays attention to such minor flaws when someone is that cute? When we went on a date the second week of the school year, guys began to hate on me. "You'll be going on a blind date," they'd joke with her, "and you won't be able to see eye to eye on anything." Even Jarvis was trying to diss me by telling Tania that I didn't have an eye for beauty.

Envious, envious, envious, I thought as I tried to ignore the haters.

Tania and I took a literature class together and the first book our teacher Ms. Best assigned was by a local writer entitled, *The Road to Faith.* They should have called it *The Road to Fate* since this book was killing me. It took me two days to read one paragraph! It was a silly book about seeing God through the eyes of a child. The author had used his ten-year-old daughter's prayer journal as the inspiration for the book. Trying to score some points for my superior analysis, I shared my disgust with Tania. "Girl, this book is juvenile, boring and a downright waste of time. I think Ms. Best is getting a cut of the profits for requiring us to read this. How in the world did the publishers allow such a literary disaster to get on the market?"

Tania looked perplexed and asked, "Which book are you talking about?"

"That dirty brown book, 'Road to Faith' we have to read," I replied.

"But that's the book my father and I wrote together."

Oops! I started praying that the earth would open up and swallow me. That night, I joyfully read the entire book in thirty minutes. I found that reading is much more fun when you have a crush on the author.

Chapter 5
It's Everybody's Business

On the third night of the revival, Pastor Livermore quoted a verse in Matthew that tells of two people working in a field when, all of a sudden, one was taken while the other was left behind.[10] The pastor explained that this is called the secret rapture, and some believe that when Jesus comes to earth again, good people all over the world will simply disappear and go to heaven while the bad folks remain here on earth. I found the perfect illustration to explain to Jarvis this idea of one taken and the other left behind, recalling the time both of us were chasing Tania Brown. I was getting the upper hand, but like a crab in a barrel, he tried pulling me down. I reminded him of the day she drove by in her father's fancy convertible Thunderbird. I obviously didn't see her pull up, so sly Jarvis tried getting into the car before me. She gently said, however, that there was only room for one, and that one was Dexter. I was taken and he was left behind. Jarvis wanted to punch me for my insightful example.

The pastor's take on the matter was that the "secret rapture" was really no secret at all because, when Jesus pays earth another visit, it will be a very public event with trumpets blowing, and everybody will see Him.[11] However, I was thrown for a loop when he also said that when Jesus shows up the second time it would be like "a thief in the night."[12] *How can there be loud trumpet sounds with every eye watching if He's like a thief?* I wondered to myself.

For Jarvis, Jesus coming like a thief simply meant that when He puts in another appearance many people will be caught off guard. Getting all worked up he said, "No thief would phone to say, 'I'll be over at 9:30 tonight. Leave the new iPod and the car keys on the kitchen counter to make my job easier.' That's why the verse in Matthew keeps talking about being ready." I was not about to tell him I thought he was right, but it's true that, in Locoville, if they knew Jesus was passing through at 4:30 on Friday afternoon, they would party and drink until 4:25 and then set aside 5 minutes to sober up and confess.

It made me cringe, though, when the pastor compared Jesus' return to a burglar at night. All I could think about were the thieving terrible twins, who, many a time, created huge messes in our tiny peaceful village. When those two clowns first set out on the crime scene, they hit up Ma Pearl's *obeah* store. Tommy broke in one night, and when Ma Pearl heard the commotion, she called downstairs and asked, "Who's that?" Thinking quickly, Tommy meowed. She thought it was a stray cat and went right back to sleep.

Timmy, wanting to get in on the action, begged his brother to tell him how to make a clean getaway when he robbed Ma Pearl's store. So Tommy warned his brother that when he was inside, he would probably bump into stuff.

Timmy asked, "What do I say if Ma Pearl hears me and asks, 'Who is that?'"

Tommy replied, "Meow like a cat."

Three nights later, Timmy was robbing the store and knocked down a bottle. Ma Pearl, again wakened by the crash, called out, "Who's that?"

Timmy answered softly, "Meow like a cat." That was his first arrest.

Chapter 6
Lets Get Quizzical

Pastor Livermore decided that preaching at the nightly services wasn't enough, so he added nightly quizzes. Little 4x8 note cards and pencils were handed out. The person who answered the most quiz questions correctly by the end of the revival would win first prize—a laptop. Second prize was a goat, and third prize was three month's worth of free pumpkins. The good pastor told us that he wanted us to share what we were learning under the tent with each other. He would ask a question, then point to someone to give an answer. The pastor promised to give all the correct answers to the questions at the end of the third quiz.[13] But often it was easy to tell right away who got it right or who blew it.

"Okay guys, first question. In the following Bible verse, I want you to find the opposite of the words 'ascend' and 'hush.' 1 Thessalonians 4:16 *'For the Lord Himself will descend from heaven with a shout, with the voice of the archangel, and with the trumpet of God; and the dead in Christ shall rise first.'* A) Descend and shout. B) Rise and silence. C) Climb and loud."

That was a no-brainer and David nailed it. "Good job, David," the pastor cheered.

He continued. "Jarvis, for our second question, find a word in the following Bible verse that is similar to these words: 'bandit, robber.' 2 Peter 3:10 '*But the day of the Lord will come like a thief, in which the heavens will pass away with a roar and the elements will be destroyed with intense heat, and the earth and its works will be burned up.*' A) Law-abiding. B) Thief. C) Prisoner."

"Silkie Stern." People snickered and poked each other.

The pastor smiled. "No name-calling please."

"But sir, you asked who were bandits and robbers!"

By this point, the pastor saw that he was in for an interesting time. He continued, "Don't forget, our focus is on the Bible and not people in the community. Now let's get into deeper waters. Question number three: Which of these phrases do you think correctly conveys what the following Bible verses are saying? Ecclesiastes 9:5-6 '*For the living know they will die; but the dead do not know anything, nor have they any longer a reward, for their memory is forgotten. Indeed their love, their hate, and their zeal have already perished, and they will no longer have a share in all that is done under the sun.*' A) The dead know they are dead and the living don't know they are alive. B) The dead know nothing because they no longer have feelings, thoughts, or memories. C) Both are incorrect."

I hope he never reads this, but the most contentious couple in Locoville, without question, was Jarvis' parents, Mavis and Big Frank. Without waiting for the pastor to point to her, Mavis answered with conviction, "It's A!"

"And how did you arrive at that?" asked Pastor Livermore.

"Well, my husband Frank sits around the house all day eating, sleeping, and talking badly about people. He's dead and doesn't even know it."

Trying hard to hide his smile, the pastor continued on. "Number four: Where was Lazarus before Christ said, 'Come forth?' John 11:43-44 '*And when He had said these things, He cried out with a loud voice, 'Lazarus, come forth.' He who had died came forth, bound hand and foot with wrappings; and his face was wrapped around with a cloth. Jesus said to them, 'Unbind him, and let him go.'* A) A roving ghost. B) In the tomb. C) Waiting for Jesus to call him down from heaven. D) Dancing in hell." When that cute, brilliant Tania answered his question, I thought she had gotten it correct since the pastor didn't comment on her answer.

It was the fifth question that made the pastor happy the quiz had ended for the evening. "Gilly, number five: How does the following Bible verse view visiting an *obeah* person, a psychic, or a fortune-teller? Isaiah 8:19 *'And when they say to you, 'Consult the mediums and the spiritualists who whisper and mutter,' should not a people consult their God? Should they consult the dead on behalf of the living?'* A) It's sensible to do only if they can give you the winning lottery numbers. B) It's fine as long as it's not too much trouble to get to their homes. C) By visiting these people, we're telling God we don't trust him."

Gilly's answer was A, and the folks there pleaded with the pastor to keep from asking for any explanation. People knew Gilly was about to ask for their birthdays in order to come up with the winning lottery numbers.

Chapter 7

If You Drop It Won't Stop

It was the end of another one of my twelve-hour workdays and I was finally dragging myself home. A minivan pulled up beside me and Grace, who worked at Small Change, Locoville's supermarket, rolled down her window. She joked, "You're working to death trying to live. But if you dropped dead now, not much would change. Things would keep right on going."

Faking surprise, I asked, "You mean, if I drop the earth won't stop?"

"Hop in," she said, slightly amused. "I'll take your tired behind home."

How nice of her, I thought. I got in and set my heavy bag on my lap. Grace's van was very fancy and luxurious. I had always wondered where a cashier at a supermarket could find the money to purchase such a vehicle.

"Do you think my van is made of cardboard?"

"Why do you ask?" I replied, taken aback by the question.

"You're still carrying that eighty-pound bag on your lap."

Tired and not thinking clearly, I said, "You've already put yourself out of the way to give me a ride. You carry me, but I'll carry my own load."

The pause that followed told me that a sermon was on its way. Grace had just been given an opening, and she was ready. She, like her father, used every opportunity, whether it was really there or not, to teach an idea from the Bible. Once, someone dialed her phone number accidentally and Grace asked him, "It's the wrong number but do you know Jesus can help you through your hard times?" Two hours later, this complete stranger was praying that Jesus would be his best friend. So I knew I was going to get the full treatment—and I was right. For the next ten minutes or so, she knew she had a captive audience.

"Many people are like you, Dex. They give their baggage to Jesus and then still insist on carrying it! Don't you know that God wants to lighten our load and give us rest? That's why God offered us a Sabbath day to rest. The day is there to teach us that there is someone greater than us who is willing and able to take care of us."

I had heard about the Sabbath from Pastor Livermore who, during the second week of the revival, said it came around every Saturday.[14] Many churches in the world celebrate their Sabbath on Sunday. However, that wasn't always the case. As he explained it, some Roman emperor hundreds of years ago had a vision, became a Christian, and tried to make Christianity as easy as possible to accept. Since many Romans worshipped the sun, he made every *Sun*-day a day off from work, making it very popular. That meant that the practice of Jesus followers' taking it easy on the seventh-day Sabbath was no longer the cool thing to do. To justify it further, the Roman Christians argued that Sunday was the day that Jesus rose from the dead, so clearly it was more sacred.

Grace wasn't one of those uppity church people who acted like she was better than everyone else. And because of this, she got away with her constant passion to share from the Bible, whenever and wherever. Her sermon went on and on as the van slowed almost to a crawl.

If You Drop It Won't Stop

These ten minutes may turn into an hour, I silently thought to myself. So to hush her up I said, "Girl, Saturday is a bad day to rest! Don't you know that it's the best day for sales?"

I should have known better, because that got Grace going on about trusting in God who was quite good at providing for people's needs. While she continued to talk about rest, I was wondering if her mouth ever got a Sabbath rest. We were coming to a stop, but before I could escape, she took me by the hand and said, "I've not always been a good Sabbath keeper, Dex. You know how on Sabbath we don't do business?"

I answered a quick yes, trying hard not to stimulate further conversation.

Without skipping a beat, Grace continued, "One Sabbath, one of the leaders at the church had a 'For Sale' sign on his minivan. It was worth at least $7500. I walked up to him and said, 'If it wasn't the Sabbath I'd ask you how much you were selling that van for.' He replied, 'If it wasn't the Sabbath I'd tell you $1235.' 'Well,' I said, 'If it wasn't the Sabbath, I'd tell you to meet me at the bank at 9:30 on Monday morning. But since it's the Sabbath, we won't discuss any business. See you on Monday.'"

Chapter 8
Sun Go Down

I couldn't understand the reason for the hype. Grace was always raving about taking Saturday off each week to spend time getting closer to God and family. She claimed that the Sabbath helps people not worry and to unwind from their tiring week. It sounded like she had a ball spending a whole day hanging out with Jesus and friends. After my ride with Grace, my curiosity got the better of me and I decided to take a stab at Sabbath keeping. I was worried that people would think I was all weird and strange to be going to church on a Saturday, so I decided to be a *secret* Sabbath keeper. Going solo and being as discreet as possible, every Saturday for an entire month I did absolutely nothing. No TV, no laundry, no selling, no buying, and I even stopped kicking it with the guys in order to just chill out. I took twelve-hour catnaps and read as much of the Bible as I could. I was confident that God was really happy that I did zilch on His day; that I eased up on work. Periodically after that, I tried keeping the Sabbath again. I thought I was doing a mighty fine job with my secret Sabbath-keeping, summer messed me up. Grace had said that, according to the Bible, a day begins in the evening. This is why Sabbath starts at sunset on Friday and ends at sunset on Saturday.[15] But during the summer, the sun sets later than it does during the rest of the year. So when I was through with the Sabbath on Saturday afternoon around the time I was used to it ending and ready to get back to having some *real* fun, the sun was still high in the sky, and it just wouldn't budge! When I realized that this was one of those lo-o-o-ng summer days, I walked around the house, practically begging the sun to set as soon as possible.

Doing nothing all day can sure stress you out! I must have been doing something wrong because all that downtime on a Saturday was killing me! I thought Grace was the most sensible person to help me through my Sabbath-keeping issues. Yeah, right. I don't know what made me tell my business to her because she was just itching to point out to me that twiddling my thumbs for 24 hours was not keeping the Sabbath. She said I was treating this sweet time as if it was a straitjacket; like God was holding me against my will. As usual, not at a loss for words, Grace went on a spiel about how I was treating this day, which was meant as a time to recharge my batteries, as if it was imprisoning me. As if I was doing God a favor when I kept it.

In the revival, Pastor Livermore was beginning to sound like Grace when he said that the Sabbath was made for man and not for God.[16] That's why, as he understood it, the practice of doing no business and resting the body is God's guideline for helping us to get the most out of the day He set aside for our good. I decided to try Sabbath keeping their way in order to figure out what was so enjoyable about setting aside a whole day to get real deep with Jesus.

Going public, I was taken aback at the interest from Gilly and David when they found out I was going to church on a Saturday. They were quite pleased to inform Mom about proper and improper Sabbath practices. One such practice they invented was that people who kept the Sabbath didn't eat all day Saturday. With delight at my expense, they helped themselves to my portion of the Saturday lunch at home.

So I was really glad to find out that the Better Living Believers, who were putting on the revival under the tent, had a weekly Saturday meal at their church called a potluck. I use to think that "potluck" was the way people locked their pots so their nosy neighbors wouldn't see what they were cooking. Boy, was I happy to be wrong about that! It was cool to see different families bringing all kind of delicious foods to share with one another.

Ever the bashful one, Big Frank, even though he'd not once showed up to any of the church meetings, was first in line to be served. He told the servers, "I eat a balanced diet; a plate in my right hand, a plate in my left." Mavis said the word "ashamed" wasn't in his dictionary.

After we had stuffed our face with the finger-licking good food, there was an afternoon program for the young and the young at heart. We played a bunch of Bible games and were told lots of stories, like the one about three boys in a big fire who didn't get burned, and the man who got thrown into a lion's den because he prayed too much. We also heard about a queen who saved God's people from being killed, and a woman warrior named Deborah.[17] I couldn't believe that, for all those weeks, I had been losing out on such good times.

One of the stories Jarvis liked the most was about a man named Jonah who tried to run away from God and got swallowed by a huge fish. When Jarvis got home that evening, he told his father Frank that when he got to heaven he was going to ask Jonah how it felt to be in the belly of that big fish.

Frank, playing the devil's advocate, asked, "So what if Jonah is in the other place?"

Jarvis replied "Then, Dad, you'll ask him for me!"

Chapter 9
Cheap Is Not the Word

Ma Pearl was once married to a man rumored to be at least twenty-five years older than she was. People often said he was "robbing the cradle" while she was "robbing the grave." Sam Pearl was a cheapskate in every sense of the word. He was the type of person who, if he got something for free, still wanted a discount.

Being cheap caused him to have a falling out with the Milk and Honey Tabernacle Church where he was a member. The church was building a community center and had become strapped for cash to finish the job. Around this time, while at a Wednesday night prayer meeting, Sam Pearl had asked the Milk and Honey Tabernacle members to pray for him. He was expecting an inheritance and was having difficulty with the probate proceedings.

"Please pray that all goes well, brothers and sisters, " he pleaded. Then, on impulse, he added, "I promise you before God to donate twenty-five percent of the inheritance I receive."

"Amen!" the folks responded, thrilled.

Not too long after this occasion, Sam Pearl stopped coming to meetings, and rumors surfaced that Sam had just been awarded a large sum of money from an inheritance. But the Tabernacle members waited in vain for the promised donation.

Pastor Swindle paid him a visit to ask him if he would still keep his promise. His excuse was that when he had no money he had the mind to give, but now that he had gotten the money, he had lost the mind.

He eventually stopped attending church altogether—until he came down with an incurable illness. The doctors gave him three months to live. Pastor Swindle started coming by to visit him at least twice a week and they slowly built a strong bond together. Sam paid off his mortgage and made sure that his insurance would cover Ma Pearl for as long as she lived. He then took every remaining penny out of his bank account and counted $87,069.65 in cold hard cash, which he kept in a shoebox under his mattress. On one of Pastor Swindle's weekly visits, he pulled out the shoebox from under his mattress and made the pastor promise to bury every last penny with him upon his death.

On the day that cheapskate died, few showed up at his funeral, and even fewer mourned. Just before the casket was closed, the pastor, with trembling hands, threw the shoebox into the coffin. Overhearing the pastor talk about the shoebox, that very night the terrible twins barely allowed the dirt to settle before they began digging. Sam was the first rich person to die in Locoville so they were expecting this to be a big score. After two long backbreaking hours, they finally reached the coffin, grabbed the shoebox, quickly refilled the hole and fled the scene.

On their way home, they talked about their plans for the stolen cash. One would buy a new red sedan and the other would go sailing in a new yacht. They eagerly opened the shoebox and pawed around. They were absolutely furious to find, instead of cash, only some shredded paper. And at the bottom of the box, hidden under the shredded paper, was a check in Pastor Swindle's handwriting, written out to Sam Pearl for $87,069.65. The pastor had kept his promise to Sam Pearl while helping Sam to keep his promise to the church. How else do you think they got the cash to finish the community center?

Chapter 10
Money Madness

The issue that bothered Big Frank the most about attending church was their constant begging for more money. What made matters worse was that on the day their dog Rufus died, his wife Mavis went to the village priest to ask if he'd do the funeral. Tamb Sing, Locoville's priest, told her that the Catholic Church does not do funeral services for dogs.

Frustrated, Mavis said, "You mean I'll have to take my $2000 and give it to the Presbyterians?"

The priest then replied, "You did not tell me that the dog was a Catholic."[18]

Like Big Frank, I used to think all preachers were crooks and cons who used the Bible to steal. I've been to a church that even had three offerings: a thank offering, a love offering, and a praise offering. I gave $1 and said, "Lord, I *love* to *thank* and *praise* You!"

Due to this low opinion of preachers and churches, during the third week of the revival, when Pastor Livermore preached a sermon about giving money, I was turned off from the get-go. I stuck my headset into my ear and tuned him out, but when I heard a lot of laughter, I pulled it out to listen. I tried to find out from David what was so funny. He refused to tell me, but held his stomach trying to control his side-splitting laughter. "You should have been paying attention," he said.

As I started listening, Pastor Livermore spoke about shady preachers and how we shouldn't allow them to cause us to lose out on our blessings. He explained that God wanted everyone who really appreciated all the good He gave them everyday to give ten percent of their income back to Him. This ten percent we give to God was called a "tide," which made me wonder what giving money had to do with big ocean waves. That was until Mavis made me put my tongue between my teeth to pronounce my "th"—making it "tithe."

The pastor spoke about a fellow named Malachi who used to go all over the place telling people that when they gave God ten percent of their money He would open up a window in heaven and give them such riches that they wouldn't know what to do with it. It seemed the pastor knew my sister Gilly was listening because he clarified that this wasn't like playing the lottery. He said that God could bless people in many different ways, like giving them health, happiness, and peace of mind.

Pastor Livermore added that he thought God had come up with the idea for the tithe in order to help us be more generous. When he explained that greed sometimes kills people and makes us less loving and kindhearted, Jarvis, up to no good as usual, started poking his mom. A while back, Mavis had begun to feel fed up with giving up ten percent of her paycheck. She later shared with Jarvis and me that she used to feel good about giving ten percent of her income when she hardly worked and her income was only $2 a week. But as God continued to bless her and she started making more money, giving Him ten percent became harder and harder. That's because her ten-percent gift to God had grown from $2 to $200 weekly. When she met with the pastor and shared with him that she wanted to pay less than the ten percent, he prayed an unusual prayer for her. "Lord, now that you have blessed Mavis by increasing her income, giving ten percent is becoming more and more difficult for her. Would you please reduce her income so that her gift of ten percent could be much less? Amen."

Pastor Livermore convinced me that giving makes life much more enjoyable. I knew this was true because I remembered Mama's example. She was always talking about how good she felt to see children, who were all grown up now, whom she'd helped through school. Us kids had not been quite so happy because she'd made us wear some no-name tennis shoes so she could also buy a pair for a neighbor's child who attended school barefoot.

I thought Mom had always been generous, but she told me that one day while she was waiting for a flight to Canada from the Piarco Airport, she saw the man sitting next to her take one of her cookies. In shock at the man's bad manners and fighting to contain her disgust, she grabbed one herself so that he would get the message to leave her cookies alone. Instead of backing off, this total stranger helped himself to another! In her fury, she refused to make eye contact with this shameless man. Then the situation moved from the sublime to the absolutely ridiculous. When there was only one cookie left in the package, Mom couldn't believe her eyes when the man took it and broke it in half. She left the empty wrapper with him and stormed off. Sometime during the flight, she opened her purse to get out her paperback novel and, much to her surprise and embarrassment, she found her own unopened package of cookies inside! She would later tell us how such experiences inspired her to become more unselfish. Somewhere in that airport was a bewildered stranger catching his flight, wondering about the crazy woman who ate his cookies with an attitude.[19]

Mom tried to instill her understanding of generosity in David and me while growing up. When David was seven years old and I was five, Mom was preparing her special burgers for dinner. It was a long day and we both were really hungry, so we began arguing over who would get the first burger. Right then, Mom saw an opportunity for us to learn a lesson. "If Jesus was sitting with us here," she said, "He would say, 'I'll let my brother have the first burger and I will wait.'"

Turning to me, David said, "Dex, you be Jesus."[20]

Chapter 11

A Sprinkle or a Dunk?

The weekend after her eviction, Ma Pearl showed up at the revival, shocking everybody. At the end of his sermon, the pastor asked if anyone wanted to invite Jesus to be a part of their life and be baptized. I used to think that "baptized" was when pastors held you under the water after saying some words about God. As villagers came down to the podium that the pastor called an altar, David said that others were crying and moving their lips as if they were praying. I couldn't understand the reason for so many tears, since no one had died or been injured. Something in the back of my head began telling me to go to the altar so I could give my life over to Jesus, but I didn't want those people to push me down into that pool and drown me.

Jarvis slipped past David and me and headed to the front. There was a lull in the proceedings and some people started gasping in shock. David whispered to me in a melodramatic tone, "It's Ma Pearl!"

Apart from being the village *obeah* woman, Ma Pearl was known for her filthy mouth and fighting dirty for her territory. This is why I didn't know if he wanted me to run, hide, or to scream out, "I'm blind! I'm blind! Please don't hurt me!" I whispered back to him, "Did she strike the pastor?" What he said next almost made me pass out. Ma Pearl went up to be baptized!

After whispering something in the pastor's ear, five minutes later she was standing at the podium. She began by saying, "This man's *obeah* is stronger than mine. I want to trust in his God." She was accompanied to the altar by Mr. S.T.

Mr. S.T. was a strange fellow. He had the letters "S-T" splashed across his forehead in what looked like a tattoo. Many said it wasn't a tattoo, but that someone had branded him. Because of his saintly manner, most thought the "S.T." meant Saint Thomas. But that was only a guess since no one really knew what those letters stood for.

In the following days, there was a buzz in the little village over those who were going to be baptized. Big Frank refused to let Jarvis take the dip because he had been sprinkled with water as a baby and was therefore already baptized. Jarvis tried to convince his father that his baby sprinkling didn't count and he now had a need and a readiness to be baptized like Jesus was. Jarvis wasn't the best-behaved kid in Locoville and I don't think that fact helped his case much.

He told his dad how the preacher spoke about a man named Matthew who followed Jesus around. In a book he wrote, Matthew said that Jesus told His followers that they needed to teach the world everything about Him, baptizing everybody into this new way of living.[21] Since a baby cannot be taught, neither could it be baptized. After a few days, Big Frank gave in and said it wouldn't hurt anything if Jarvis got baptized again. "But ain't no use having them people dunk you down in that river; you just need to be sprinkled."

Jarvis then explained to Frank that the pastor had told us that baptism stood for dying and being buried with Jesus, and when a person went all the way down into the water, it was like going down into the grave and coming up out of the water was like being raised from the dead.[22] Frank thought this was a bunch of nonsense and insisted that sprinkling was the same as being buried.

A Sprinkle or a Dunk?

A day or so later after this heated discussion, the pastor and Mr. S. T. came to visit Big Frank at his house. This visit came about because the pastor, in addition to asking people to come down to the altar to be baptized, also gave out little cards allowing the person to check off whether they wanted prayer, a visit from the pastor, or baptism. One of the cards the pastor received had Big Frank's name written on it and the box requesting a pastoral visit and baptism had been checked.

I had my suspicions as to how Big Frank's name got on that card seeing as he was definitely taken aback by the unexpected visitors. The first thing they noticed was the huge plate of lobster in one hand and his beer and a remote control in the other. Big Frank felt too embarrassed to tell the pastor that he had no idea he was coming. He had not attended any of the nightly meetings and would never have signed any card asking for a visit or baptism.

Forty-five minutes later, Big Frank still hadn't decided to be baptized, and he began to look for an escape from the grueling conversation. Jarvis popped his head in to see what was going on and tried to escape before Frank could see him, but it took only one hard look to have him slouching in the chair beside his dad. "I don't mind checking out baptism, but I won't be baptizing my hands because I still need to choke a few people," Frank said, glaring menacingly at Jarvis.

Grateful for the distraction, Frank then quickly turned the conversation off of himself and on to Jarvis. He told his visitors that this boy was too bad to be baptized. "He'll go down a dry devil and come back up a wet one," adding, "I don't know if God can change such mischief-makers."

Then Mr. S.T., who had been silent up to now, spoke up and told his story. About twenty years before, he used to go around stealing sheep in Locoville. Some villagers eventually caught him, held him down and branded his forehead with the letters "S-T" meaning "sheep thief." After he became a follower of Jesus, people forgot his old lifestyle and thought the S.T. meant Saint Thomas. "My baptism was to tell everyone that I had changed and had become a new person with God. Many a day I would still hear those sheep baaing to be stolen. But since I had been dipped in baptism, I was now living for God and for the people who expected better of me."

Big Frank was so impressed with how Mr. S. T.'s dunk in the water had kept him from stealing sheep that he looked at Jarvis and said, "There's still hope for you, but they may have to hold you under the water for a long, long time."

Chapter 12
Stop the Clowning

The characters that assembled for the second nightly quiz were a crazy bunch. Everybody wanted the laptop, of course. Jarvis was acting like the goat, taunting Tania, telling her that that goat was what she would win, while Gilly was giving me advice for what I could do with the three-month supply of pumpkins that she was sure I would be stuck with. Mavis wanted that laptop so badly that she forced Big Frank to come to the meeting, took two quiz cards and filled out both, one with Frank's name and the other with her own.

"Okay friends, let's get cracking," the pastor began. "Tania, question number one: From the following phrases, I want you to find which ones best describe the Sabbath. Exodus 20:8-11 *'Remember the Sabbath day, to keep it holy. Six days you shall labor and do all your work, but the seventh day is the Sabbath of the LORD your God; in it you shall not do any work, you or your son or your daughter, your male or your female servant or your cattle or your sojourner who stays with you. For in six days the LORD made the heavens and the earth, the sea and all that is in them, and rested on the seventh day; therefore the LORD blessed the Sabbath day and made it holy.'* A) The seventh day. B) Rest from work. C) Church in the morning, then off to the ball game and supermarket in the afternoon."

"Piece of cake," she said smugly, which is why I started wondering if she was just showing off.

The pastor continued with David. "Tell me which of the following are good Sabbath-keeping practices. Nehemiah 10:31 *'As for the peoples of the land who bring wares or any grain on the Sabbath day to sell, we will not buy from them on the Sabbath.'* And Nehemiah 13:15 *'In those days I saw in Judah some who were treading wine presses on the Sabbath, and bringing in sacks of grain and loading them on donkeys, as well as wine, grapes, figs, and all kinds of loads, and they brought them into Jerusalem on the Sabbath day. So I admonished them on the day they sold food.'* A) Bargaining for minivans. B) Shopping, since Saturday is the best day for sales. C) Resting and refraining from buying and selling."

David didn't get his answer out because, in the middle of his response, Big Frank said, "I agree that the Sabbath is a good thing, but it's only for those Jewish people." In response, the pastor had us read Mark 2:27, which says, *"The Sabbath was made for man, and not man for the Sabbath."* The pastor then looked at Big Frank and said, "M-A-N was a strange way to spell Jew."

Using that same Bible verse, he continued. "Jarvis, number three. Now how should we interpret Mark 2:27? A) Sabbath-keeping is doing God a favor because it's made for Him. B) Sabbath is like being imprisoned, so people should pray for early sunsets on Saturday afternoons. C) Sabbath is for our enjoyment since it was made for us."

I don't know if Jarvis was trying to get himself in trouble but instead of answering the question, he asked, "If people always sat around the house all week doing nothing, would the Sabbath still mean anything to them?"

Pastor Livermore ignored the question and asked Big Frank, "Number four: Who is baptism good for? Matthew 28:19 *'Go therefore and make disciples of all the nations, bap-*

tizing them in the name of the Father and the Son and the Holy Spirit.' John 3:5 *'Jesus answered, 'Truly, truly, I say to you, unless one is born of water and the Spirit, he cannot enter into the kingdom of God.'* A) Babies. B) Those who don't care to learn anything about God. C) Unclean animals. D) People who desire to love and follow Jesus."

Frank began, "I'm choosing C." There was a loud groan from the crowd. Frank was having an on-going argument with Pastor Livermore over what he should or should not eat. The pastor had showed him in the Bible that God didn't want certain animals to be eaten by people, but Frank wasn't having any of it. "I'm choosing C because if baptism means you are washed and cleansed and a new creature, then I could baptize my pig and lobster to make them clean so they'll be good to eat!"

What a wise man that Livermore was. With an amused look, ignoring Frank, he smiled and turned to me to ask the next question. "Number five, Dex: Choose three opposite words that symbolize baptism. Romans 6:3-4 *'Or do you not know that all of us who have been baptized into Christ Jesus have been baptized into His death? Therefore we have been buried with Him through baptism into death, in order that as Christ was raised from the dead through the glory of the Father, so we too might walk in newness of life.'* A) Full of life, awakened from the grave, sealed in a tomb. B) Death, burial, resurrection. C) Sleepy, cremated, resurrection." This one was a brainteaser, but I was sure I got it right.

Pointing to Ma Pearl, the pastor asked, "Number six: What is a tithe? Malachi 3:10 *'Bring the whole tithe into the storehouse, so that there may be food in My house, and test Me now in this,' says the LORD of hosts, 'if I will not open for you the windows of heaven, and pour out for you a blessing until it overflows.'* A) $1 of everything you receive. B) Ten percent of your income. C) Whatever you give based on the mood you're in."

Ma Pearl chose A and said that her deceased husband, Sam Pearl, before he died, once told her that a tithe is $1 of $10, and $1 of $50, and $1 of $100.

Chapter 13

Pigging Out

It was Christmas and Mom did what she does best—bring dead animals to life. Every year we enjoyed delicious ham and eggs, along with punchacrima, a smooth-tasting milky drink with a strong alcohol kick to it—especially if Jenny Thomas was making it. Sometimes Mama would give a taste to us kids to "clean out the worms" from our stomachs. I would tell her that I had worms as large as birds.

As I hurried to join the family for Christmas dinner, my stomach rumbled and my mouth watered. I was already savoring the taste of Mom's good ol' Christmas cooking. But suddenly it hit me. I had already made up my mind to be a Better Living Believer. I planned to go down to the river for baptism, so I didn't eat pork or drink alcohol anymore! Oh no!

Then I struck upon a brilliant plan. *I'll just eat the pork and drink the punchacrima, and hope that another revival will come around so I could get baptized then.* (Any time other than Christmas, of course!) Then I had to be honest with myself. *Didn't you decide, in front of all those people under the tent, to treat your body really good by not drinking alcohol and eating unhealthy food?*

Rats! Right about then I was really hating on Pastor Livermore for teaching me about Moses. Moses had written a bunch of stuff about what kinds of meats were good for people to eat and which weren't. I wished I could tear out from my Bible Leviticus 11 and Deuteronomy 14—chapters written by old Moses. They stated that the only animals safe to eat were those with "cloven hoofs" and that "chew its cud" (that would be cows, goats and sheep), as well as only fish with "scales and fins" (which would mean no lobsters and crab).

When I first shared these Bible verses with Silkie's mom, Sister Stern, she copped an attitude and said, "How old-school and archaic!" She said that when Jesus came on the scene He taught that if you knew how to pray really well and said some good blessings over those animals you could eat as you please. She was the type of Christian who went around casting out demons from everything. One afternoon she had come over to our house to eat, and prayed that God would cast out the calories and fat from the pork chops before devouring it. With stomach growling and mouth salivating, her words were sounding pretty good. I thought to myself, *After all, the pastor is always saying there's freedom in Christ!* So I walked to that dinner table with a swagger.

"Here's the non-pork, non-alcoholic table, Dex," Mom said.

"What?!" *Should I tell her I've changed my mind about being baptized?*

David couldn't wait for the prayer to bless the food and was already chomping on a ham bone. "Dex, this is a bad time to be a Better Living Believer; this is some good pork ribs. You know, if there ain't no pork eating in heaven, you need to eat all you can right here and right now," he teased.

But I couldn't disappoint my family; they'd think I was the biggest hypocrite in the world. Right then, I was thinking I'd been a real fool to share my decision for baptism so quickly.

I was so caught up in my thoughts that I didn't hear when my mom called me, of all people, to offer the blessing. "Dex, where are you?" Mom asked.

Well, I sure wasn't "in the Spirit!"

"Lord, bless our meal and let it do our bodies good. In Jesus name, amen."

After that prayer, I had to keep it real. How could pork and punchacrima do any good for my body? Besides, the vegetarian casserole rocked! Where in the world did Mom get the recipe? Maybe this vegetarian eating wasn't going to be as bad as I thought!

Big Frank was too much of a gentleman to turn down a free meal, so he was at our dinner table with his wife Mavis. He was brooding as he shared my non-pork dishes because he was under strict doctor's orders not to eat pork and other high cholesterol foods. But every so often, one could see him eyeing the ham, especially when his wife wasn't looking. He used to tell Mavis that he was the healthiest man alive. He knew this to be true because he'd had twenty-eight diseases and beat every one.

I was shocked to see that Sister Stern also took her place among the non-pork eaters. That day I learned she had not only given up unhealthy meats, but she was even more hardcore than I had ever been. She had gone meatless altogether! What in the world happened? Previously, both Moses and I had tried and failed to convince her that pork eating was bad. Life is so interesting! Only a few months earlier she was showing me every verse she could find in the Bible to prove that Christians could eat whatever they felt like. But now she insisted, "The pigs are dying because we kill and eat them. We are dying young because it's killing us to eat them. I'm just trying to live a bit longer." With real regret she told us, "I used to use the words of life to bring about my own death."

She had decided that anything with a face or a mother shouldn't be eaten. Her new slogan was, "If you want to be as strong as an ox, eat what the ox eats, but don't eat the ox."[23] Glaring at the mountain of food before Big Frank, Sister

Stern said, "Some people have to wait for the *doctor* to tell them to stop eating what God has *already* said wasn't healthy for people to eat."

Frank replied under his breath, "Today, the only things I *won't* be eating will be the things I *drink*."

Chapter 14

Saint Tommy?

It was a strange but sad day in Locoville when Tommy, the taller of the twins, fell from a mango tree while stealing a few, broke his neck and died. You would have thought that people would have been rejoicing and dancing in the streets, but it was as if they had put aside their outrage at his many crimes to mourn his loss. Someone even raised enough money to hire some of the local rummies as mourners. These hired mourners were supposed to pretend to have had good relations with the dead so as to comfort the families with their wailing. Island wakes always had lots of free alcohol. No wonder Big Frank gladly took the job as a mourner. He was heard joking, "Who else is going to die so I can get more free rum?"

Eventually, he got dead drunk and didn't even know who he was mourning. As he chatted up Tommy's aunt, he absentmindedly asked, "What was your nephew's name again?" He ended up being the first person I'd ever heard of that got thrown out of a funeral.

The pastor had a difficult task in doing the funeral sermon. What good could he say about such a wicked fellow? What made things worse was that Tim, Tommy's twin, wanted the pastor to say that his brother was a saint.

The pastor began by speaking about the power of the resurrection and that those who were used to hearing Jesus' voice when they were alive would hear Him when He comes for the second time and calls them out of the grave.[24] When the pastor paused, Tim, who sat on the podium with him, whispered, "Don't forget to say he was a saint."

The pastor continued, saying that when Jesus returns to this earth, He will raise up His friends who are sleeping in their graves and, as fast as you can wink, they'll immediately change from people who grow old, get sick and die, to super-humans that never get tired and live forever and ever. "Then," he said, "what a scene that will be, as millions of people meet Jesus in the air!"[25]

Tim again butted in, insisting, "Say he was a saint."

Continuing to ignore Tim, the pastor told the congregation that there are two resurrections—the first for the righteous and the second for the wicked. All who love God would be a part of the first resurrection. [26] So when those who are buddies with God die, their friends and family don't need to lose hope since they'll get to be together again.[27]

Finally, Tim, not getting what he wanted, pulled the pastor's coattail and whispered quite loudly, "You're forgetting to say that he was a saint!"

The pastor finally began to list Tommy's most outstanding attributes. "This man was a no-good, low-down, rotten thief, but in comparison to his brother he was a saint."[28]

Chapter 15
Hell, No?

Hell is a confusing subject. Sometimes I hear people saying, "It's as hot as hell!" and at other times they'll say, "It's as cold as hell." Most of the preachers that I heard while growing up in Locoville preached about hell to scare people into their churches. They would literally make my blood run cold as they described in awful detail how people who ended up in hell would howl and scream as their flesh rotted away but they could never die.

However, during the last week of the revival, Pastor Livermore taught that God doesn't make people suffer forever since hell is a place where people burn to ashes and are no more. He explained that he came to this understanding because the word Jesus used for hell is Gehenna, which was some big old garbage dump outside of Jerusalem where everybody would throw away all their trash and even the dead bodies of people whose families couldn't afford a proper burial place. Criminals who were put to death were often thrown in there as well where, along with the trash, they were burned to ashes.

The pastor's explanation of hell was really helpful because all I knew about hell up to that point was from what my high school history teacher used to tell us about the Aztecs who lived in Mexico a long time ago. He said that their belief was that hell wasn't just a single place of torture and burning. The Aztecs believed in nine stages of hell that included crossing an ocean filled with sharks, climbing a treacherous mountain, and walking through fire. The horror list went on and on. I just had to tease my teacher, "So when someone tells me to go to hell, I should ask them, 'which part?'"

Pastor Livermore described how people could end up losing out on living with God forever. He told about how Jesus once drew lessons from farm management to teach the men that followed him around. Jesus said He was like a vine and the people that took seriously his ideas about life and carried them out were like the branches growing from that vine.[29] But people who didn't care to live out His ideas were separating themselves from Him—from the vine. When they did this, they would end up losing nourishment, wither up, fall from the tree, then be thrown into a big fire like dead wood and be gone forever.

While Pastor Livermore was helping me clean up all my wrong ideas about hell, Jarvis whispered to Mavis, "Did you hear that, Mom? Hell is a place where bad dead people burn up. Nobody will be burning in any big old oven for a thousand bazillion years. God is only cleaning up the place from all those dead bodies." He was teasing his mom because she was always sending Frank to burn forever in hell for all sorts of stuff.

Before Mavis could disagree with the pastor, however, he drove home his point with another example from the Bible. A fellow named Ezekiel said that even the devil would burn to ashes and be no more.[30] Although Mavis was beginning to be persuaded, she was happy Frank wasn't there to hear this sermon so that she could continue to send him to the hottest parts of hell.

Chapter 16
Crooked Colorful Characters

One night, the good teacher Pastor Livermore had Mavis give the opening prayer before the quiz. Praying with one eye on Frank she said, "Lord, isn't it sad that some people live to see a whole lot of hell and then still end up there?"

The pastor used this comment to jump into his next series of questions. "Number one," he began. "What is not true about these Bible verses? Revelation 20:14-15 *'And death and Hades were thrown into the lake of fire. This is the second death, the lake of fire. And if anyone's name was not found written in the book of life, he was thrown into the lake of fire.'* A) The lake of fire is a literal never-ending burning place. B) The lake of fire stands for the second death. C) None of the above."

No one was surprised to find out that Mavis chose A. What a hard nut to crack!

It seemed that parrot sales were slow, so Silkie had come to the meeting that night. The pastor spotted him and asked him the second question. "Number two: According to the following Bible verses, those who push God out of their lives will ... what? Malachi 4:1 *'For behold, the day is coming, burning like a furnace; and all the arrogant and every evildoer will be chaff; and the day that is coming will set them ablaze,' says the LORD of hosts, 'so that it will leave them neither root nor branch.'* A) Burn forever and ever without end. B) Burn until they are no more. C) Since they're from Locoville they'll be given a free pass."

Avoiding the question, Silkie commented that even if burning forever wasn't true, people still needed to see the consequences of their bad behavior in order to live right. "One time, my three-language-speaking parrot was cursing people," he said. " I warned him and warned him to stop, but he wouldn't listen. Finally, I put him in the deep freeze for ten minutes to cool off, and when I took him out, the parrot said, 'Now that I see what happened to the turkey, I'll never use those words again.' And Pastor," Silkie declared, "the parrot is now the only born-again bird in the world and is still going for only $28.75!"

The pastor, with a doubtful look on his face, continued with Tania. "Okay, my sister, number three: Based on the following Bible verse, when Jesus returns, who shall come out of the grave to live with him forever? John 5:28, 29 *'Do not marvel at this; for an hour is coming in which all who are in the tombs shall hear His voice and shall come forth; those who did the good deeds to a resurrection of life, those who committed the evil deeds to a resurrection of judgment.'* A) Those that did good deeds. B) Those who were evil. C) Those who get their friends to call them saints." The competition was getting stiffer by the moment since I was sure Tania had flunked that question.

The next question fell to me. "Number four: At Christ's second coming, which of the following statements are false? 1 Corinthians 15:51-53 *'Behold, I tell you a mystery; we shall not all sleep, but we shall all be changed, in a moment, in the twinkling of an eye, at the last trumpet; for the trumpet will sound, and the dead will be raised imperishable, and we shall be changed. For the perishable must put on the imperishable, and this mortal must put on immortality.'* A) The righteous shall change from people who grow old, get sick and die, to super-humans that never get tired and live forever and ever. B) The change shall take place in the blink of an eye. C) The rapid change would occur right after the secret rapture."

I answered, but David said he couldn't tell from the pastor's body language if I had gotten it right.

Tamb Sing, the priest who did the funeral service for Frank's dog Rufus, showed up that night, most likely to see which of his members were under the tent. The pastor warmly greeted him and asked him the next question. "Okay, my friend Sing, number five: Based on the following verses, which of these meats are considered clean for human consumption? Deuteronomy 14:6,9 '*And any animal that divides the hoof and has the hoof split in two and chews the cud, among the animals, that you may eat...These you may eat of all that are in water: anything that has fins and scales you may eat.*' A) A grey dog. B) Lobster and crabs. C) Pork. D) Chicken and beef."

Tamb Sing chose C. The pastor said he wasn't surprised that he chose that answer because they had a running joke between them. "Friends," the pastor shared, "once the good priest asked me when I would come home and eat some pork with him. I told him, "At your wedding, dear sir!"

Postscript
A Day Without Drama?

Before we drove down to the river for the baptisms, Pastor Livermore gave the highly anticipated announcement of the quiz winners. My sister Gilly won the laptop computer. I had a hard time being happy for her since she chose all the answers by closing her eyes and saying, "eeny meeny miney mo". Tania came in a close second and got the goat that Ma Pearl, who was much more generous than her stingy husband had been, had donated. The goat warmed up to me as if we had known each other for a long time. Come to think of it, he acted suspiciously similar to our old pet Shane. Tania didn't keep the goat, however, but traded him to Silkie for his three-language-speaking, born-again parrot.

I came in third, so I was the proud winner of three months worth of pumpkins. There was a delay in getting the bird, however, and Tania, who had no patience whatsoever, offered to trade me her promised three-language parrot for my three months of pumpkins only a few days later. She had no idea how I had spent nights dreaming of owning such a rare bird! I quickly agreed and the transfer was completed. I never did get the parrot, however, since Silkie kept saying it was either back in his deep freeze or still on its break.

The baptism celebration was wonderful. Even Big Frank went down into the water and said that he was giving up all his bad behavior in exchange for a brand new life with Jesus. He knew now that people didn't burn in hell forever and ever but said that he loved God more than he was afraid of hell. And yes, even his hands were baptized since he was through with all that choking business. Mavis was happy that his mouth and stomach also took the dip since Frank had also given up the idea of baptizing his pork and lobster to make them okay to eat.

After Frank, the next to be dunked was Mavis and then Sister Stern. Sister Stern had been riding to the meeting every night with Mavis and they had become good friends. She now had Mavis sold on her vegetarian recipes, which she claimed Mother Eve ate before she got tricked by the talking serpent.[31]

Silkie only wished his mother, Sister Stern, had become a vegetarian earlier. One day, Silkie had left his three-language-speaking parrot at his mom's home and found it had disappeared on his return. His mother had run out of chicken and had cooked the bird. He complained and asked, "Mom how could you cook my parrot? Didn't you know he spoke three different languages?"

Sister Stern replied, "If he spoke three languages he should have spoken up!"[32] It was weeks after the baptism before Silkie admitted to me the reason behind the delay in receiving my prized parrot.

The fourth to be dipped was Ma Pearl. After a time, she re-opened her store and was now selling "Jesus loves you" lotion and hair grease called "Growing in Grace." Just like Mr. S. T. had said, the good news about Jesus can change even the worst of us. That's how Jesus converted the crooks and clowns of Locoville.

Good Stuff

Other Works by
D. Roderick Thomas

From Rags to Ruin:
Stories and Sermons by a Street Preacher
Empathy, Empowerment and a Radical Vision

This book narrates the journey of seven people working in a tiny ministry in downtown Oakland, CA. They will inspire you with the stories and real-life moments from their journey in the life transformations of hundreds who are homeless, maimed and marginalized on the streets of this American city.

Those troubled by the violence and crime in large cities, and concerned with impoverished children and the homeless during long winter nights, will gain practical skills in reaching the needy. It is a must-read for those who want to learn how to love the unlovable, cultivate a heart of compassion, and resuscitate hope in the hopeless. It is a stimulating manual that gives not only challenging insight, but also down-to-earth, hands-on skills for today's urban ministry. The practical examples and steps shared about helping people back on their feet are doable and repeatable anywhere.

In a world where growing disparities between rich and poor are unraveling the social fabric that binds us together, *From Rags to Ruin* reminds us that accompanying the poor and marginalized in their struggle for life is not, in the end, about their transformation, but about ours.

Learning through Laughter series

**Part 1—*Learning through laughter:*
Truth through Fun**

**Part 2—*Learning through Laughter:*
Funny Stories in Stressful Times**

This two-disk comedy series will both motivate and strengthen you through the hard stuff of life. You'll learn to laugh at your everyday struggles while finding ways to cope. Thomas tells hilarious stories about wisdom and a pumpkin, a Christian lion, the blessings and burdens of blindness, and walking a straight line in a crooked world.

To order these products, and for motivational talks, preaching engagements, or comedy shows, contact D. Roderick Thomas at www.grandadvent.org or phone the church office at 510/452-0785. You can email Thomas at dex4jesus@hotmail.com.

The audio version of *Messy Revival: Funny Stories for a Change* is also available on a two-CD or a two-DVD set, and *From Rags to Ruin is* on a two-CD set. Both can be obtained at the address listed above.

Treasure Hunt

1 Treasure Hunt Website on Trinidadian folklore: http://www.tntisland.com/folklore.html

2 Ecclesiastes 9:4, 5, 10 For whoever is joined with all the living, there is hope; surely a live dog is better than a dead lion. [5] For the living know they will die; but the dead do not know anything, nor have they any longer a reward, for their memory is forgotten. [6] Indeed their love, their hate and their zeal have already perished, and they will no longer have a share in all that is done under the sun. … [10] Whatever your hand finds to do, do it with all your might; for there is no activity or planning or knowledge or wisdom in Sheol where you are going

Psalms 88:10-12 Will You perform wonders for the dead? Will the departed spirits rise and praise You? Selah. [11] Will Your loving kindness be declared in the grave, Your faithfulness in Abaddon? [12] Will Your wonders be made known in the darkness? And Your righteousness in the land of forgetfulness?

Psalm 115:17, 18 The dead do not praise the LORD, Nor do any who go down into silence; [18] But as for us, we will bless the LORD From this time forth and forever. Praise the LORD!

3   Genesis 3:1-7 Now the serpent was more crafty than any beast of the field which the LORD God had made. And he said to the woman, "Indeed, has God said, 'You shall not eat from any tree of the garden'?" [2] The woman said to the serpent, " From the fruit of the trees of the garden we may eat; [3] but from the fruit of the tree which is in the middle of the garden, God has said, 'You shall not eat from it or touch it, or you will die.'" [4] The serpent said to the woman, "You surely will not die! [5] For God knows that in the day you eat from it your eyes will be opened, and you will be like God, knowing good and evil." [6] When the woman saw that the tree was good for food, and that it was a delight to the eyes, and that the tree was desirable to make one wise, she took from its fruit and ate; and she gave also to her husband with her, and he ate. [7] Then the eyes of both of them were opened, and they knew that they were naked; and they sewed fig leaves together and made themselves loin coverings.

4   Deuteronomy 18:10-14 There shall not be found among you anyone who makes his son or his daughter pass through the fire, one who uses divination, one who practices witchcraft, or one who interprets omens, or a sorcerer, [11] or one who casts a spell, or a medium, or a spiritist, or one who calls up the dead. [12] For whoever does these things is detestable to the LORD; and because of these detestable things the LORD your God will drive them out before you. [13] You shall be blameless before the LORD your God. [14]

For those nations, which you shall dispossess, listen to those who practice witchcraft and to diviners, but as for you, the LORD your God has not allowed you to do so.

Leviticus 19:28 You shall not make any cuts in your body for the dead nor make any tattoo marks on yourselves: I am the LORD.

5   Dr. K. S. Wiggins sermon tape

6   John 11:11-14, 38-45 This He said, and after that He said to them, "Our friend Lazarus has fallen asleep; but I go, so that I may awaken him out of sleep." [12] The disciples then said to Him, "Lord, if he has fallen asleep, he will recover." [13] Now Jesus had spoken of his death, but they thought that He was speaking of literal sleep. [14] So Jesus then said to them plainly, "Lazarus is dead. ... [38] So Jesus, again being deeply moved within, came to the tomb. Now it was a cave, and a stone was lying against it. [39] Jesus said, "Remove the stone." Martha, the sister of the deceased, said to Him, "Lord, by this time there will be a stench, for he has been dead four days." [40] Jesus said to her, "Did I not say to you that if you believe, you will see the glory of God?" [41] So they removed the stone. Then Jesus raised His eyes, and said, "Father, I thank You that You have heard Me. [42] I knew that You always hear Me; but because of the people standing around I said it, so that they may believe that You sent Me." [43] When He had said these things, He cried out with a loud voice, "Lazarus, come forth." [44] The man who had died came forth, bound hand and foot with wrappings, and his face was wrapped around with a cloth. Jesus said to them, "Unbind him, and let him go." [45] Therefore many

of the Jews who came to Mary, and saw what He had done, believed in Him.

Job 14:12-14 So man lies down and does not rise. Until the heavens are no longer, He will not awake nor be aroused out of his sleep. [13] Oh that You would hide me in Sheol, That You would conceal me until Your wrath returns to You, That You would set a limit for me and remember me! [14] If a man dies, will he live again? All the days of my struggle I will wait until my change comes.

7   *Worth Every Drop: A Journey into the Heart of God* by Jonathan Henderson, pg. 55. Published Jonathan Henderson

8   Jonathan Henderson

9   *Ibid.*

10 Matthew 24:39-42 That is how it will be at the coming of the Son of Man. [40] Two men will be in the field; one will be taken and the other left. [41] Two women will be grinding with a hand mill; one will be taken and the other left. [42] "Therefore keep watch, because you do not know on what day your Lord will come.

11 Revelation 1:7 Behold, He is coming in the clouds, and every eye will see Him, even those who pierced Him; and all the tribes of the earth will mourn over Him. So it is to be. Amen.

Matthew 24: 27 For just as the lightning comes from the east and flashes even to the west, so will the coming of the Son of Man be.

1 Thessalonians 4:16-18 For the Lord Himself will descend from heaven with a shout, with the voice of the archangel and with the trumpet of God, and the dead in Christ will rise first. [17] Then we who are alive and remain will be caught up together with them in the clouds to meet the Lord in the air, and so we shall always be with the Lord. [18] Therefore comfort one another with these words

12   2 Peter 3:10 But the day of the Lord will come like a thief, in which the heavens will pass away with a roar and the elements will be destroyed with intense heat, and the earth and its works will be burned up.

1 Thessalonians 5:1-7 Now as to the times and the epochs, brethren, you have no need of anything to be written to you. [2] For you yourselves know full well that the day of the Lord will come just like a thief in the night. 3 While they are saying, "Peace and safety!" then destruction will come upon them suddenly like labor pains upon a woman with child, and they will not escape. [4] But you, brethren, are not in darkness, that the day would overtake you like a thief; [5] for you are all sons of light and sons of day. We are not of night nor of darkness; [6] so then let us not sleep as others do, but let us be alert and sober. [7] For those who sleep do their sleeping at night, and those who get drunk get drunk at night.

13   Did you win big? Answers to the quiz questions:

Quiz #1: 1) A 2) B 3) B 4) B 5) C

Quiz #2: 1) A B) 2 C) 3 C) 4 D 5) A 6) B

Quiz #3: 1) B 2) B 3) A 4) C 5) D

14 Exodus 20:8-11 "Remember the sabbath day, to keep it holy. [9] " Six days you shall labor and do all your work, [10] but the seventh day is a sabbath of the LORD your God; in it you shall not do any work, you or your son or your daughter, your male or your female servant or your cattle or your sojourner who stays with you. [11] "For in six days the LORD made the heavens and the earth, the sea and all that is in them, and rested on the seventh day; therefore the LORD blessed the sabbath day and made it holy.

Luke 4:16 And He came to Nazareth, where He had been brought up; and as was His custom, He entered the synagogue on the Sabbath, and stood up to read.

Acts 13:14, 42-45 But going on from Perga, they arrived at Pisidian Antioch, and on the Sabbath day they went into the synagogue and sat down. …[42] As Paul and Barnabas were going out, the people kept begging that these things might be spoken to them the next Sabbath. [43] Now when the meeting of the synagogue had broken up, many of the Jews and of the God-fearing proselytes followed Paul and Barnabas, who, speaking to them, were urging them to continue in the grace of God. [44] The next Sabbath nearly the whole city assembled to hear the word of the Lord. [45] But when the Jews saw the crowds, they were filled with jealousy and began contradicting the things spoken by Paul, and were blaspheming.

Acts 16:13 And on the Sabbath day we went outside the gate to a riverside, where we were supposing that there would be a place of prayer; and we sat down and began speaking to the women who had assembled.

Acts 17:2-5 And according to Paul's custom, he went to them, and for three Sabbaths reasoned with them from the Scriptures, ³ explaining and giving evidence that the Christ had to suffer and rise again from the dead, and saying, "This Jesus whom I am proclaiming to you is the Christ." ⁴ And some of them were persuaded and joined Paul and Silas, along with a large number of the God-fearing Greeks and a number of the leading women. ⁵ But the Jews, becoming jealous and taking along some wicked men from the market place, formed a mob and set the city in an uproar; and attacking the house of Jason, they were seeking to bring them out to the people.

Matthew 24:20 "But pray that your flight will not be in the winter, or on a Sabbath.

15 Genesis 1:5, 9,13, 20 God called the light day, and the darkness He called night. And there was evening and there was morning, one day. ... ⁹ Then God said, " Let the waters below the heavens be gathered into one place, and let the dry land appear"; and it was so. ... ¹³ There was evening and there was morning, a third day. ... ¹⁹ There was evening and there was morning, a fourth day. ...²⁰ Then God said, "Let the waters teem with swarms of living creatures, and let birds fly above the earth in the open expanse of the heavens."

16 Mark 2:27 Jesus said to them, "The Sabbath was made for man, and not man for the Sabbath.

17 Daniel 3; 6; Esther 4; Judges 4; Jonah 2

18 Internet story

19 *Ibid.*

20   *Ibid.*

21   Matthew 28:18-20 And Jesus came up and spoke to them, saying, "All authority has been given to Me in heaven and on earth. [19] "Go therefore and make disciples of all the nations, baptizing them in the name of the Father and the Son and the Holy Spirit, [20] teaching them to observe all that I commanded you; and lo, I am with you always, even to the end of the age."

22   Romans 6:3, 4 Or do you not know that all of us who have been baptized into Christ Jesus have been baptized into His death? [4] Therefore we have been buried with Him through baptism into death, so that as Christ was raised from the dead through the glory of the Father, so we too might walk in newness of life.

23   *Enjoy It: New Lifestyle* series, by Jorge Pamplona, published Editorial Safeliz, Argentina, pg. 12-20.

24   John 5: 28, 29 Do not marvel at this; for an hour is coming, in which all who are in the tombs will hear His voice, [29] and will come forth; those who did the good deeds to a resurrection of life, those who committed the evil deeds to a resurrection of judgment.

25   1 Thessalonians 4:17 Then we who are alive and remain will be caught up together with them in the clouds to meet the Lord in the air, and so we shall always be with the Lord.

26   Daniel 12:2 Many of those who sleep in the dust of the ground will awake, these to everlasting life, but the others to disgrace and everlasting contempt.

Revelations 20:5, 6 The rest of the dead did not come to life until the thousand years were completed. This is the first resurrection. [6] Blessed and holy is the one who has a part in the first resurrection; over these the second death has no power, but they will be priests of God and of Christ and will reign with Him for a thousand years.

27 1 Thessalonians 4:13-16 (see above)

28 Ravi Zechariah sermon tape

29 John 15:1-7 "I am the true vine, and My Father is the vinedresser. [2] Every branch in Me that does not bear fruit, He takes away; and every branch that bears fruit, He prunes it so that it may bear more fruit. [3] You are already clean because of the word which I have spoken to you. [4] Abide in Me, and I in you. As the branch cannot bear fruit of itself unless it abides in the vine, so neither can you unless you abide in Me. [5] I am the vine, you are the branches; he who abides in Me and I in him, he bears much fruit, for apart from Me you can do nothing. [6] If anyone does not abide in Me, he is thrown away as a branch and dries up; and they gather them, and cast them into the fire and they are burned. [7] If you abide in Me, and My words abide in you, ask whatever you wish, and it will be done for you."

30 Ezekiel 28:18 "By the multitude of your iniquities, In the unrighteousness of your trade You profaned your sanctuaries. Therefore I have brought fire from the midst of you; it has consumed you, and I have turned you to ashes on the earth In the eyes of all who see you. [19] All who know you among the peoples are appalled at you; you have become terrified and you will cease to be forever."

31 Genesis 3:6 When the woman saw that the fruit of the tree was good for food and pleasing to the eye, and also desirable for gaining wisdom, she took some and ate it. She also gave some to her husband, who was with her, and he ate it.

32 Cleophus LaRue sermon tape